# BILLIE HOLIDAY

**WISE PUBLICATIONS**
LONDON/NEW YORK/PARIS/SYDNEY/COPENHAGEN/MADRID

GW00730034

995

EXCLUSIVE DISTRIBUTORS:
**MUSIC SALES LIMITED**
8/9 FRITH STREET,
LONDON W1V 5TZ, ENGLAND.
**MUSIC SALES PTY LIMITED**
120 ROTHSCHILD AVENUE,
ROSEBERY, NSW 2018,
AUSTRALIA.

ORDER NO.AM91356
ISBN 0-7119-3615-3

COMPILED BY PETER EVANS
NEW ENGRAVINGS BY THE PITTS

BOOK DESIGN BY STUDIO TWENTY, LONDON
COMPUTER MANAGEMENT BY ADAM HAY EDITORIAL DESIGN

PHOTOGRAPHS COURTESY OF
REDFERNS AND PICTORIAL PRESS

PRINTED IN THE UNITED KINGDOM BY
HALSTAN & CO LIMITED, AMERSHAM, BUCKINGHAMSHIRE.

# THAT OLE DEVIL CALLED LOVE

*Words & Music by Doris Fisher & Allan Roberts*

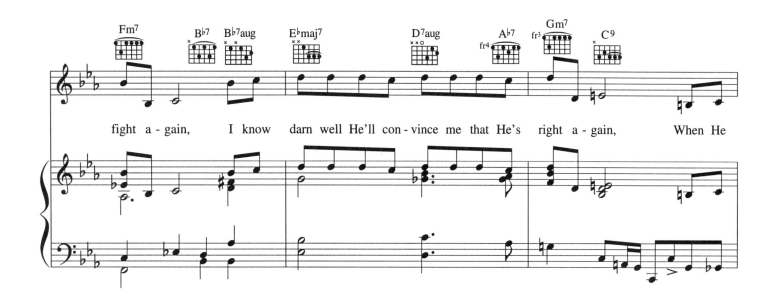

fight a - gain, I know darn well He'll con - vince me that He's right a - gain, When He

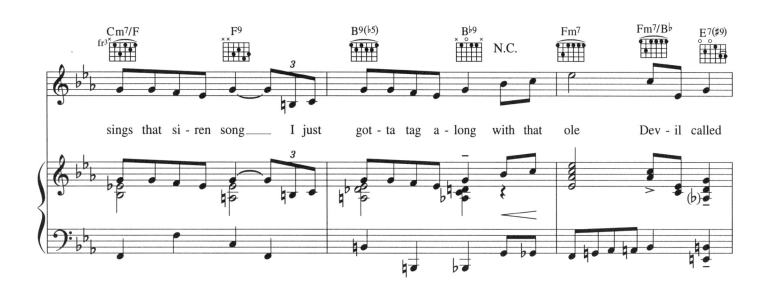

sings that si - ren song____ I just got - ta tag a - long with that ole Dev - il called

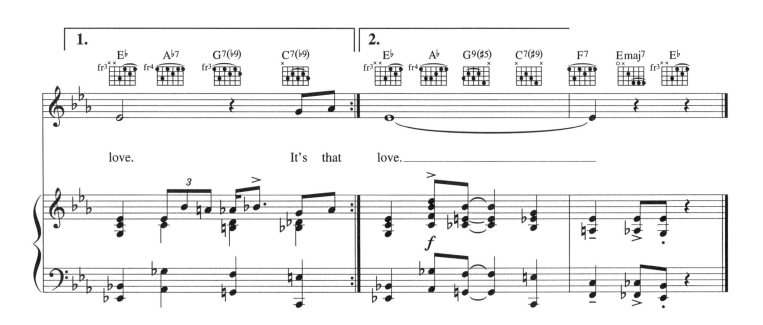

love. It's that love.____

# THE LADY SINGS THE BLUES

*Words by Billie Holiday*
*Music by Herbie Nichols*

pain in your heart,_____ when you get a bad start,_____ when you and your

man have to part._____ I ain't gon-na just_____ sit a-

round_____ and cry,_____ and now I know I won't die_____ be-cause I love him._____

La - dy sings the blues,_____ she's got 'em bad,_____

she feels so sad, But now the world will know, she's nev-er gon-na sing them no more. no more.

# A FINE ROMANCE

Music by *Jerome Kern*
Words by *Dorothy Fields*

She: (1)  A fine ro-mance! with no kiss-es! A fine ro-mance, my friend,
She: (2) (A) fine ro-mance! my good fel-low! You take ro-mance, I'll take
He: (3) (A) fine ro-mance! with no kiss-es! A fine ro-mance, my friend
He: (4) (A) fine ro-mance! my dear Duch-ess! Two old fo-gies who need

this is! We should be like a cou-ple of hot to-
Jel - lo! You're calm - er than the seals in the Arc - tic
this is! We two should be like clams in a dish of
crutch - es! True love should have the thrills that a health - y

-ma - toes,_____ But you're as cold as
O - cean,_____ At least they flap their
chow - der;_____ But we just fizz like
crime has!_____ We don't have half the

yes - ter - day's mashed po - ta - toes._____ A
fins to ex - press e - mo - tion._____ A
parts of a Seid - litz pow - der._____ A
thrill that the "March of Time" has!_____ A

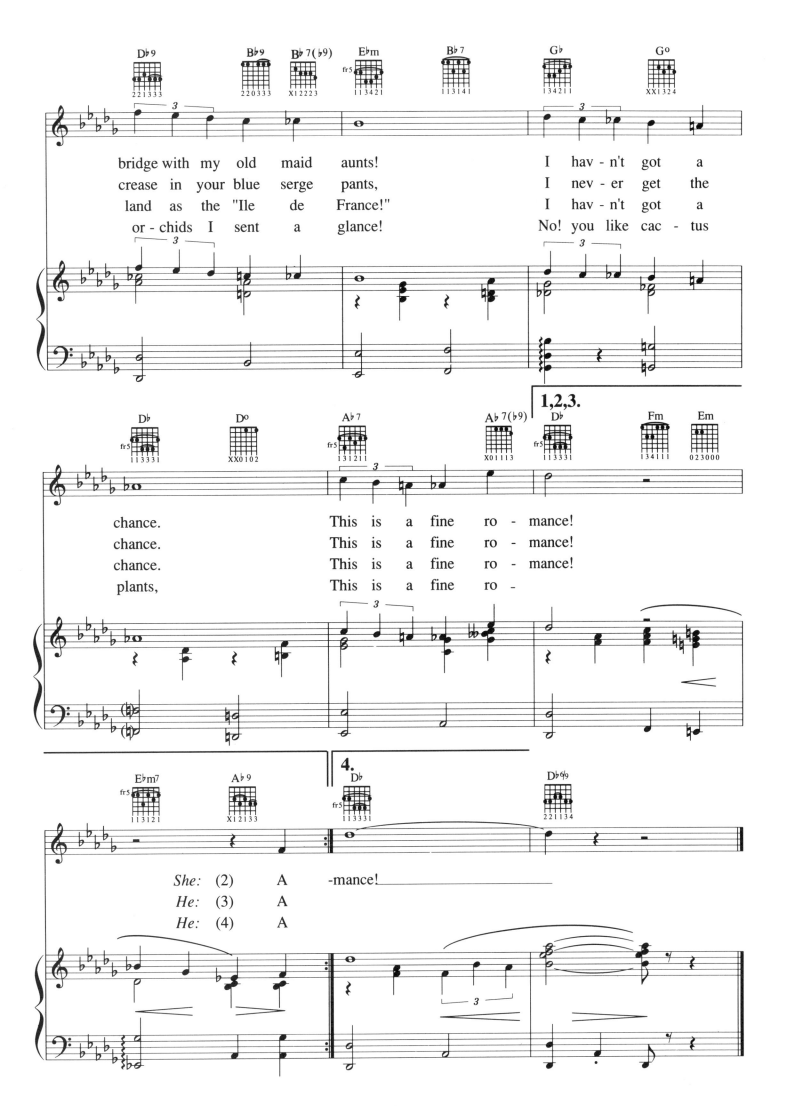

bridge with my old maid aunts! I hav-n't got a
crease in your blue serge pants, I nev-er get the
land as the "Ile de France!" I hav-n't got a
or-chids I sent a glance! No! you like cac - tus

**1,2,3.**

chance. This is a fine ro - mance!
chance. This is a fine ro - mance!
chance. This is a fine ro - mance!
plants, This is a fine ro -

**4.**

*She:* (2)  A  -mance!
*He:* (3)  A
*He:* (4)  A

15

# EAST OF THE SUN (AND WEST OF THE MOON)

*Words & Music by Brooks Bowman*

wish that we could live up in the sky,_____ Where we could find a place a - way up high,_____ To live a - mong the stars, the sun, the moon, Just

you and I._____ East of the sun_____ and west of the moon,_____ We'll build a dream-house__ of love, dear. Near to the sun in the day, Near to the moon at night, We'll

17

stars we'll find A har-mo-ny of life to a love-ly tune,

East of the sun and west of the moon,

dear, East of the sun and west of the

1. moon.

2. moon.

# CAN'T HELP LOVIN' DAT MAN

*Music by Jerome Kern*
*Words by Oscar Hammerstein II*

mine.                                    Tell me he's la  -  zy,

tell me he's slow, ___        tell me I'm cra - zy,        may-be I know, ___

Can't        help        lov-in' dat man ___ of  mine.

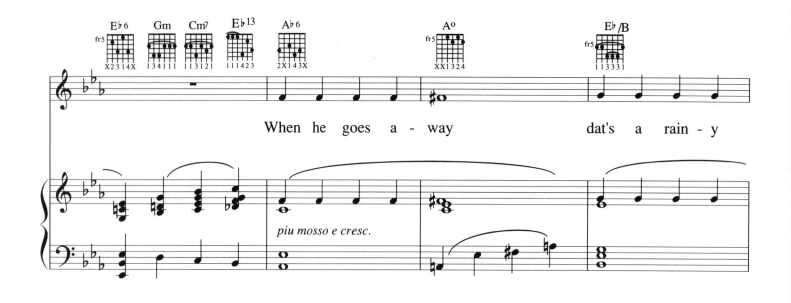

When he goes a - way dat's a rain - y

*piu mosso e cresc.*

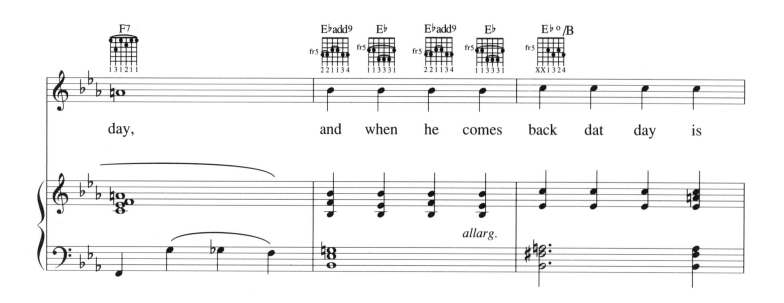

day, and when he comes back dat day is

*allarg.*

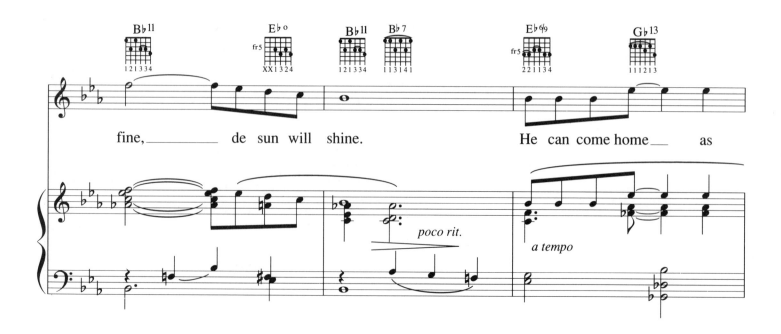

fine,_____ de sun will shine. He can come home___ as

*poco rit.*

*a tempo*

22

late as can be,___ home wid-out him___ ain't no home to me,___

Can't help lov-in' dat man___ of mine.

mine._____

# LOVER MAN (OH WHERE CAN YOU BE)

Words & Music by Jimmy Davies,
Roger Ram Ramirez & Jimmy Sherman

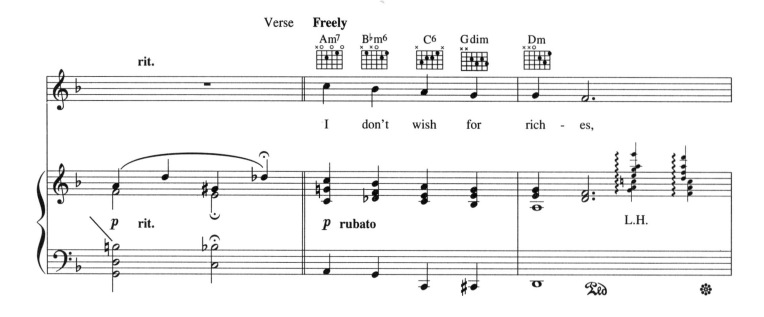

I don't wish for rich - es,

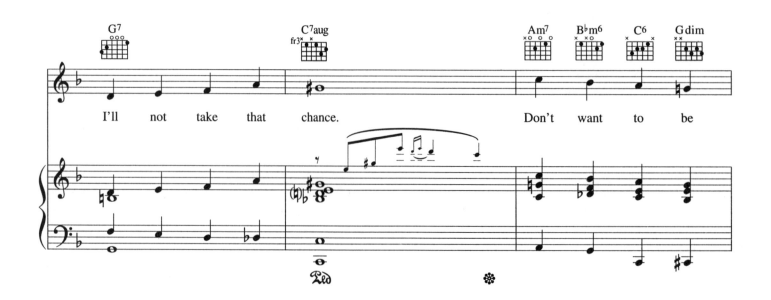

I'll not take that chance. Don't want to be

**Chorus** **Blues tempo**

pray'r that you'll make love to me, Strange as it seems.

Some day we'll meet and you'll dry all my tears,___ Then whis-per sweet lit-tle

things in my ears,___ Hug-gin' and a kiss-in', Oh what we've been miss-in',

Lov-er man, oh where can you be? be?

# I'LL GET BY

*Words by Roy Turk*
*Music by Fred E. Ahlert*

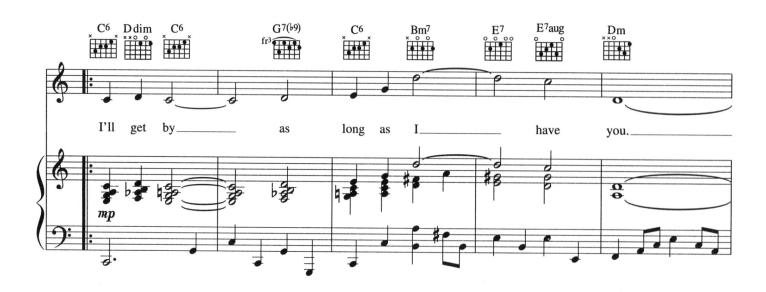

I'll get by ____ as long as I ____ have you. ____

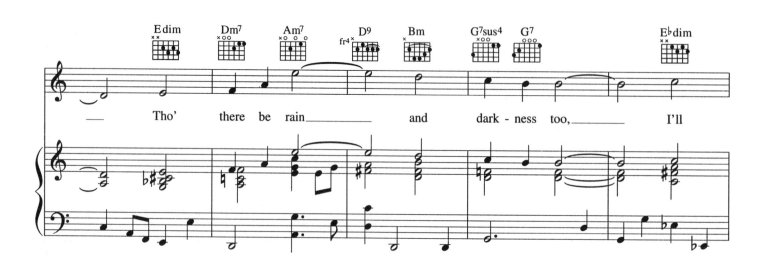

____ Tho' there be rain ____ and dark-ness too, ____ I'll

# GEORGIA ON MY MIND

Words by Stuart Gorrell
Music by Hoagy Carmichael

Mel-o-dies bring mem-or-ies that lin-ger in my heart,___

Make me think of Geor-gia, Why did we ev-er part?___

Some sweet day when blos-soms fall and all the world's a song,___

# MEAN TO ME

*Words & Music by Roy Turk & Fred E. Ahlert*

# P.S. I LOVE YOU

*Words by Johnny Mercer*
*Music by Gordon Jenkins*

Moderately

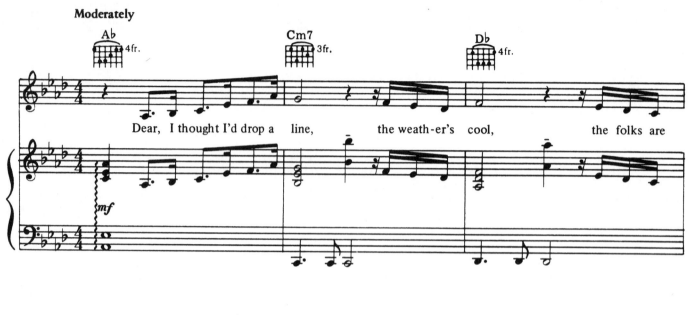

Dear, I thought I'd drop a line, the weath-er's cool, the folks are

fine; I'm in bed each night at nine.

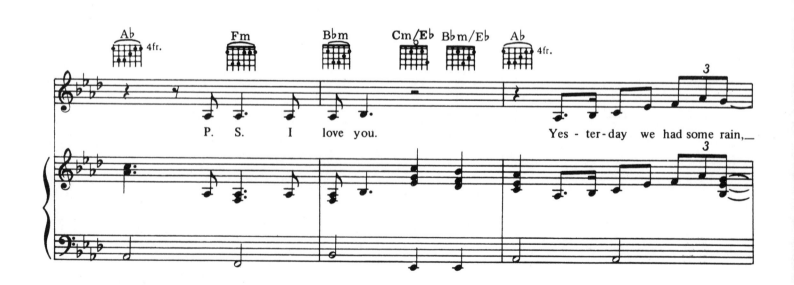

P. S. I love you. Yes-ter-day we had some rain,___

but all in all, I can't com-plain;

was it dust-y on the train? P. S. I love you.

Inst. Write to the Brown's just as soon as you're a-ble, they came a-round to

call. I burned a hole in the din-ing room ta-ble,

and let me see,___ I guess that's all.___ Noth-ing left for me to say,___

and so I'll close, but by the way,___

ev'ry-bod-y's think-ing of you, P. S. I love you.

*To Coda* ⊕

*D. S.* 𝄋 *al Coda* ⊕

*Coda*

P. S. I love you.

*rit.*

38

# STARS FELL ON ALABAMA

*Words by Mitchell Parish*
*Music by Frank Perkins*

na-tion___ a sit-u-a-tion___ so hea-ven-ly,___ A fai-ry land where no one else could

en-ter,___ and in the cen-tre___ just you and me, dear. My heart beat like a

ham-mer, my arms wound a-round you tight, and stars fell on Al-a-

ba-ma last night. night.

41

# TAIN'T NOBODY'S BIZ-NESS IF I DO

*Words & Music by Porter Grainger & Everett Robbins*

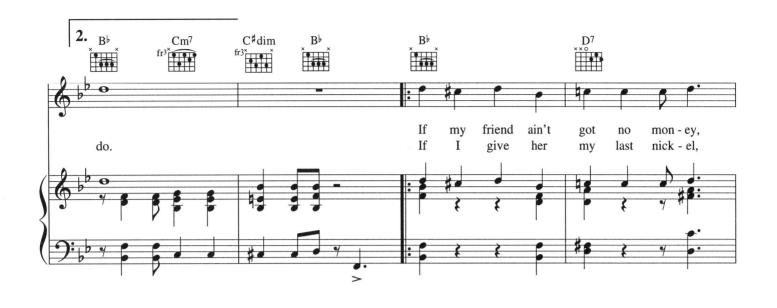

If my friend ain't got no mon-ey,
If I give her my last nick-el,

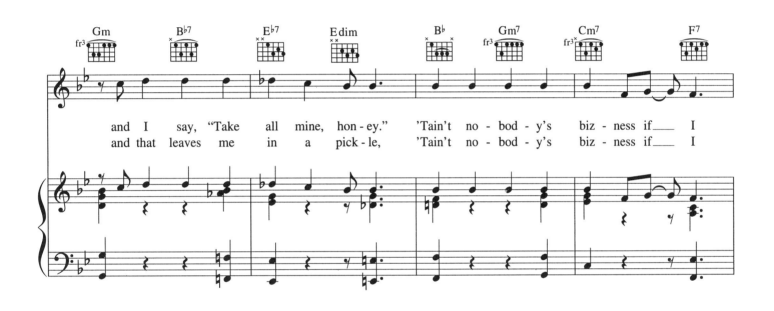

and I say, "Take all mine, hon-ey." 'Tain't no-bod-y's biz-ness if___ I
and that leaves me in a pick-le, 'Tain't no-bod-y's biz-ness if___ I

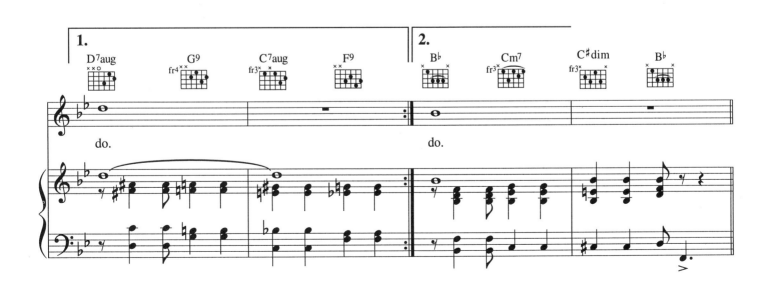

do.

do.

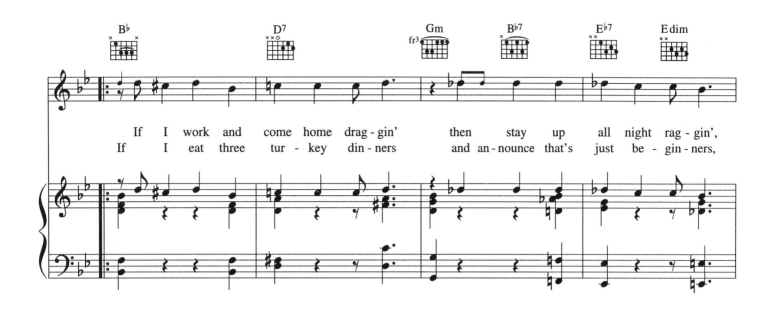

If I work and come home drag-gin' then stay up all night rag-gin',
If I eat three tur-key din-ners and an-nounce that's just be-gin-ers,

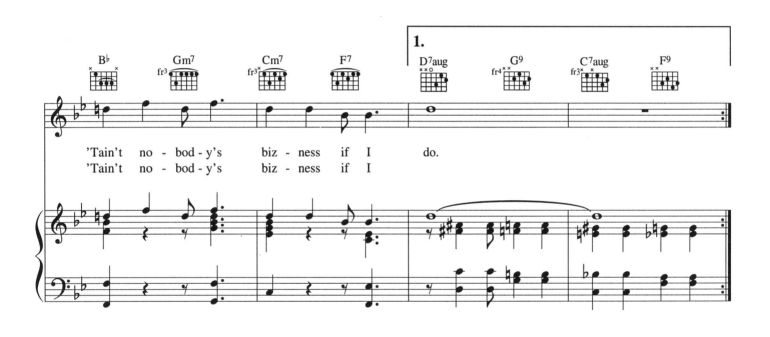

1.

'Tain't no-bod-y's biz-ness if I do.
'Tain't no-bod-y's biz-ness if I

2.

do.

If I date a
If I par-ty,

real style set-ter, but go home with some-one bet-ter, 'Tain't no-bod-y's
stay out drink-in', and buy me a ten-grand Lin-coln, 'Tain't no-bod-y's

**1.**

biz-ness if I do. do.

biz-ness if I

If I feed my wife ba-lo-ney,

and don't pay my al-i-mo-ny, 'Tain't no-bod-y's biz-ness if___ I

# THE VERY THOUGHT OF YOU

*Words & Music by Ray Noble*

I don't need your pho-to-graph, To keep by my bed;
I hold you re-spon-si-ble, I'll take it to law,

Your pic-ture is al-ways in my head.
I nev-er have felt like this be-fore.

I don't need your por-trait, dear, To call you to mind,
I'm su-ing for dam-ag-es, Ex-cus-es won't do,

For sleep - ing or wak - ing, dear,__ I find;_____
I'll on - ly be sat - is - fied__ with you;_____

REFRAIN

The ver - y thought of you,_____ And I for - get to do,_____

The lit - tle or - di - na - ry things that ev' - ry - one

ought to do._____ I'm liv - ing in a kind of

*poco rit.*

*p-mf*

day - dream, I'm hap - py as a king, And fool - ish tho' it

may seem, To me_____ that's ev' - ry - thing._____ The mere i -

dea of you,_____ _____ The long - ing here for you,_____

_____ You'll nev - er know how slow the mo - ments go 'till I'm

near to you,_____ I see your face in ev'ry

flow - er; Your eyes in stars a - bove,_____

*poco rit.*

It's just the thought of you,___ The ver - y thought of you, my love._____

*a tempo*

The ver - y love._____

*poco rit.*

L.H.

# YOU'VE CHANGED

*Words by Bill Carey*
*Music by Carl Fischer*

re - a - lise you ev - er cared.____ You've changed, you're

not the an - gel I once knew, No need to tell me that we're

through, It's all o - ver now____ you've changed.____

**1.**

**2.** *poco rit.*

You've

*mf* *poco rit.* *pp*

# STORMY WEATHER

*Words by Ted Koehler*
*Music by Harold Arlen*

Don't know why ___ there's no sun up in the sky, Storm-y weath-er, ___ since my man and I ain't to-geth-er, ___ Keeps rain-in' all ___ the time, ___

# I CAN'T GIVE YOU ANYTHING BUT LOVE

*Words by Dorothy Fields*
*Music by Jimmy McHugh*

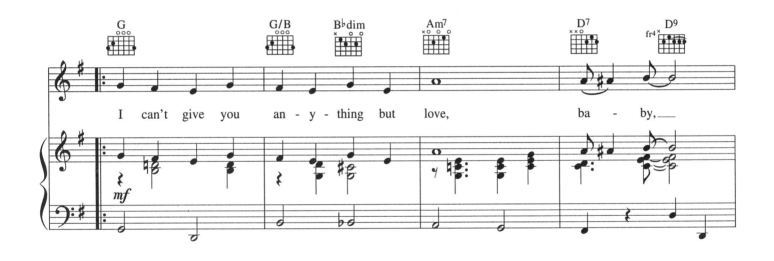

I can't give you an-y-thing but love, ba - by, ___

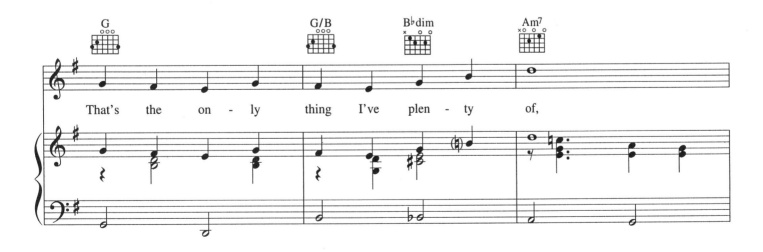

That's the on-ly thing I've plen-ty of,

Wool-worth does-n't sell, ba - by, Till that luck-y

day you know darn well, ba - by,___

1.

I can't give you an - y - thing but love.

2.

I can't give you an - y - thing but love.

# TIME ON MY HANDS

Words by Harold Adamson & Mack Gordon
Music by Vincent Youmans

bove.＿＿＿＿ To bring me con - so - la - tion, You're my in - spi - ra - tion,
aim.＿＿＿＿ The moon up - on us gaz - es, While I seek for phras - es,

This is my im - ag - i - na - tion. Time on my hands,＿＿＿＿
Dear, with which to sing your prais - es.

You in my arms,＿＿＿＿

No - thing but love _____ in view; _____

Then if you fall, _____

Once and for all, _____ I'll see my dreams _____

_____ come true.

Mo - ments to spare, _____ for some - one you care _____ for, One love af - fair _____ for two. _____ With time on my hands _____ And you in my arms _____ And

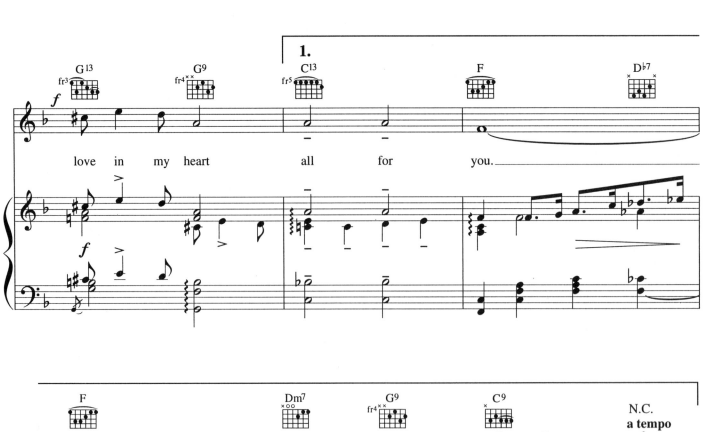

love in my heart all for you.

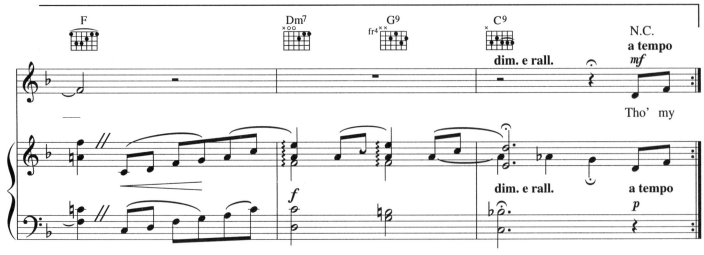

Tho' my

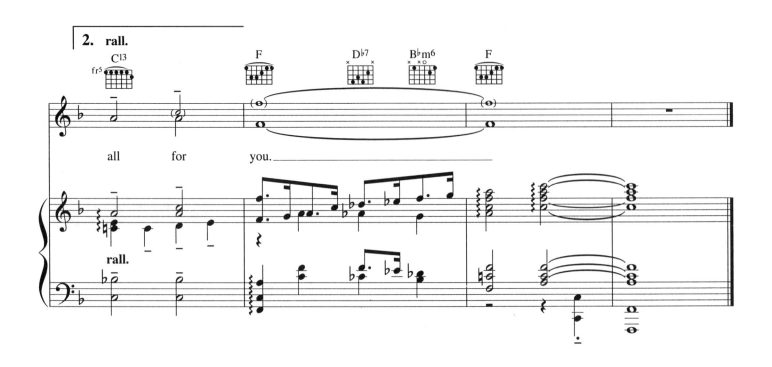

all for you.

# I'LL BE AROUND

Words & Music by Alec Wilder

I'll be a-round_____ no mat-ter how_____ you treat me now,

I'll be a-round from now on.

Your lat - est love_____ can nev - er last,_____ And when it's past, I'll be a - round when he's gone. Good - bye a - gain, and if you find a love like mine Just now and

then drop a line to say you're feel-ing fine, And when things go wrong, per-haps you'll see you're meant for me, So I'll be a-round when he's gone.

gone. gone.

# EMBRACEABLE YOU

*Music by George Gershwin*
*Words by Ira Gershwin*

fore. What was it that con - trolled_____ me?
wall. My nose I used to turn_____ up

What kept my love - life lean? My in - tu - i - tion told__
When you'd be - siege my heart; Now I com - plete - ly burn__

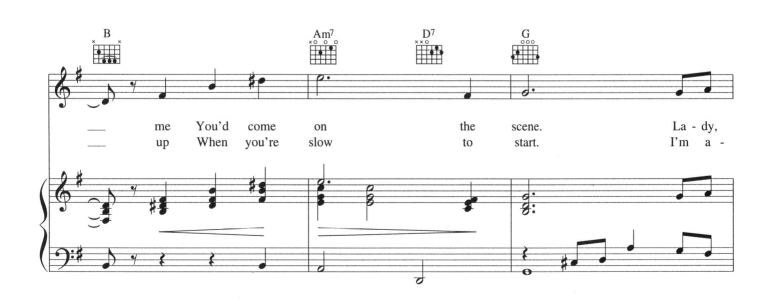

___ me You'd come on the scene. La - dy,
___ up When you're slow to start. I'm a -

lis - ten to the rhy - thm of my heart - beat, And you'll get just what I
fraid you'll have to take the con - se - quen - ces; You've up - set the ap - ple

**Chorus**
**Rhythmically**

mean.
cart.

Em - brace me, My sweet em -
Em - brace me, My sweet em -

brace - a - ble you!_____ Em - brace me, You ir - re -
brace - a - ble you!_____ Em - brace me, You ir - re -

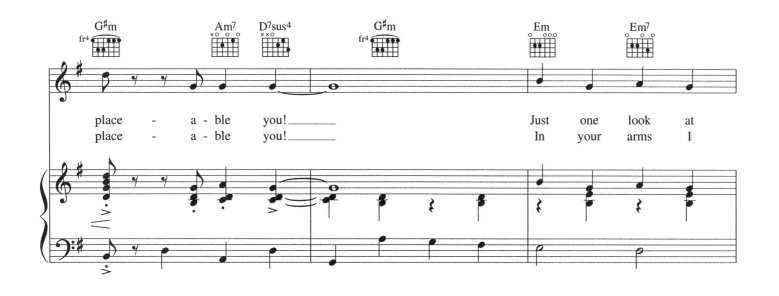

place - a - ble you!_____ Just one look at
place - a - ble you!_____ In your arms I

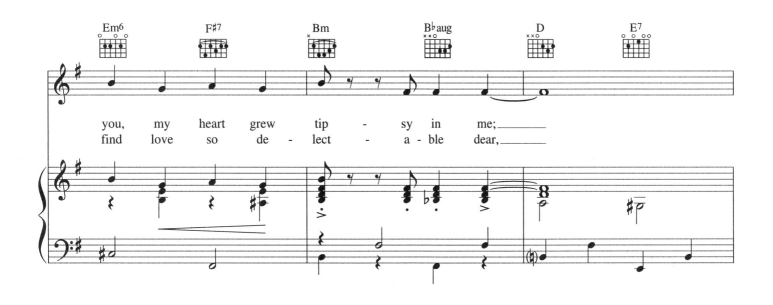

you, my heart grew tip - sy in me;_____
find love so de - lect - a - ble dear,_____

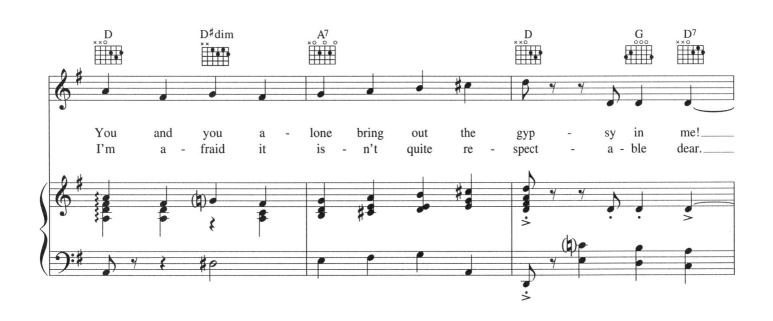

You and you a - lone bring out the gyp - sy in me!_____
I'm a - fraid it is - n't quite re - spect - a - ble dear._____

I love all the man - y
But hang it! Come on, let's

charms a - bout you;_____
glo - ri - fy love!_____

A - bove all
Ding dang it!

I want my arms a - bout you._____
You'll shout, "En - core!" if I love._____

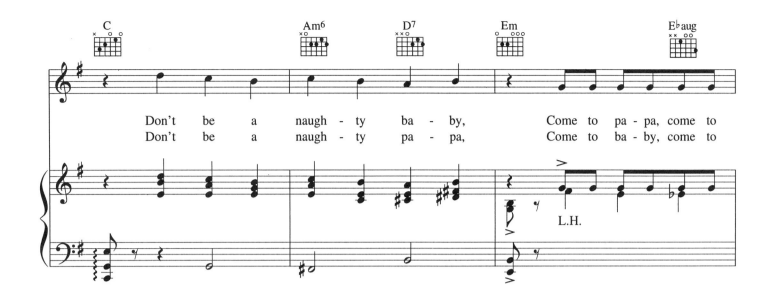

Don't be a naugh - ty ba - by,  Come to pa - pa, come to
Don't be a naugh - ty pa - pa,  Come to ba - by, come to

pa - pa, do!   My sweet em - brace - a - ble
ba - by, do!   My sweet em - brace - a - ble

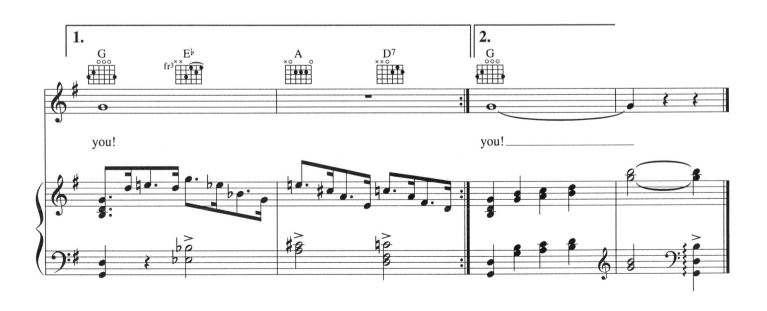

**1.** you!

**2.** you!

# VIOLETS FOR YOUR FURS

Words by Tom Adair
Music by Matt Dennis